The Recorder Player's Collection

Book Five : Descant
Selected & Edited by Colin Hand

Kevin Mayhew

We hope you enjoy *The Recorder Player's Collection Book 5*.
Further copies of this and the other books in the series are available
from your local music shop.

In case of difficulty, please contact the publisher direct:

The Sales Department
KEVIN MAYHEW LTD
Rattlesden
Bury St Edmunds
Suffolk IP30 0SZ

Phone 0449 737978
Fax 0449 737834

Front Cover: *Watermeadows near Salisbury* by John Constable (1776-1837).
Reproduced by courtesy of the Board of Trustees
of the Victoria & Albert Museum, London.

Cover designed by Juliette Clarke and Graham Johnstone.
Picture Research: Jane Rayson

First published in Great Britain in 1992 by Kevin Mayhew Ltd.

© Copyright 1992 Kevin Mayhew Ltd.

ISBN 0 86209 301 5

All or part of these pieces have been arranged by
Colin Hand and are the copyright of Kevin Mayhew Ltd.

Series Music Editor: Anthea Smith.

Printed and bound in Great Britain.

Contents

COLIN HAND (b. 1929), who arranged the music in this book, composes extensively for both professional and amateur players. His works include choral, orchestral and chamber music, as well as pieces for the recorder in which he has specialised. His music enjoys regular performances all over the world.

After many years as a teacher and lecturer, he now examines for the Trinity College of Music, London.

TWO MASQUE DANCES

Anon. early 17th century

I ADSON'S MASQUE

Allegretto

II WILSON'S LOVE

Più mosso

D.C. senza ripet.

7

MINUET IN G

Johann Sebastian Bach (1685-1750)

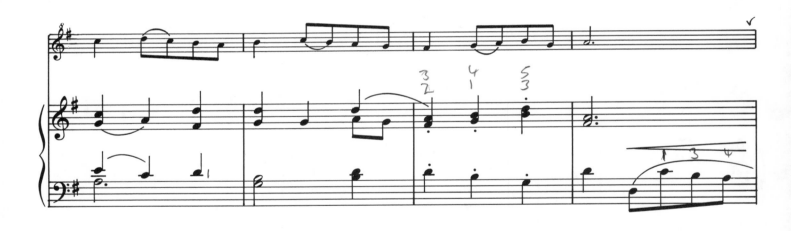

9

ALLEGRETTO from Divertimento K. 229

Wolfgang Amadeus Mozart (1756-1791)

11

HUMORESKE No. 7

Antonín Dvořák (1841-1904)

RIGAUDON AND MENUET

Georg Philipp Telemann (1681-1767)

LIBERTY BELL

John Philip Sousa (1854-1932)

(senza Ped.)

MINUET AND TRIO

James Hook (1746-1827)

ITALIAN SONG

Peter Ilyich Tchaikovsky (1840-1893)

THE TRIUMPHING DANCE
from 'Dido and Aeneas'

Henry Purcell (1659-1695)

RONDINO

Antonio Diabelli (1781-1858)

WALTZ from 'Coppélia'

Léo Delibes (1836-1891)

ARIA from 'The Water Music'

George Frideric Handel (1685-1759)

BALLET MUSIC from 'Rosamunde'

Franz Schubert (1797-1828)

THE CARMAN'S WHISTLE

William Byrd (1543-1623)

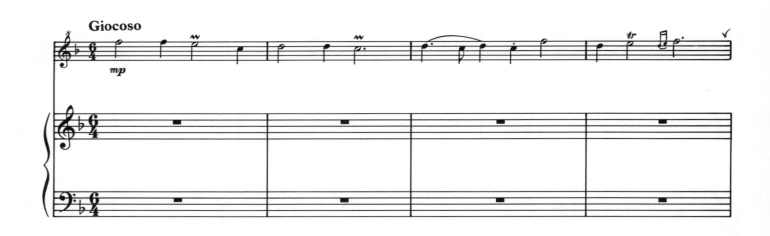

TWO SONGS from 'The Mikado'

Arthur Sullivan (1842-1900)

48